Chinese Folk Tales （Ⅰ）
中国民俗故事（上）

Adapter: Zhao Jie

改编：赵杰

Illustrator: Sun Yuguang, Zhang Ming

绘画：孙玉广、张明

Translator: Guo Bingke

翻译：郭冰珂

中國民俗故事

DOLPHIN BOOKS
海 豚 出 版 社

First Edition 2005

ISBN 7-80138-539-X

© Dolphin Books, Beijing, 2005

Published by Dolphin Books
24 Baiwanzhuang Road, Beijing 100037,China

Printed in the People's Republic of China

"Happiness" Upside Down

"福" 倒 了

When New Year comes, people in China hang the character "Happiness" upside down on the door. In Chinese, "upside down" is a homonym for "to arrive", so this is a pun for "happiness arrives."

大年三十的时候，家家户户都会把一个倒着的"福"字贴在门上。因为"倒"和"到"字同音，"福'倒'了"说起来就像"福'到'了"的意思。

中國民俗故事

This custom started in the Ming Dynasty, before which, no one hung "Happiness"upside down.

在明朝以前，老百姓门上贴的福字都是正的，那么，倒贴福字这个习俗是怎么来的呢？

It was said that the first emperor of the Ming Dynasty Zhu Yuan Zhang often went into the city disguised as an ordinary citizen.

传说，明朝开国皇帝朱元璋经常化装成平民到民间私访。

One day, Emperor Zhu Yuan Zhang heard a family criticizing him. He got very angry and turned the character "Happiness" on their door upside down to mark the house. He decided to kill the family on the night of New Year's Eve.

有一天，朱元璋听到一家人正在说他的坏话，他生气极了，就把这家门上的福字倒过来作为记号，准备在除夕晚上派人把这家人杀光。

中國民俗故事

When the Emperor got back to the palace, he was still angry.

朱元璋回到皇宫后，仍然非常生气。

Empress Ma asked him what had happened. He told her the whole story and how he had marked the family. He said, "After this incident, no one will dare to speak ill of me."

他的妻子马皇后问他怎么回事，他就把这件事告诉了她，还恶狠狠地说："从今往后，再也没人敢说我的坏话了。"

The kindhearted Empress Ma came up with an idea to avert the tragedy. She gave an order that every family should hang "Happiness"upside down on the door.

善良的马皇后听了，为了避免这场灾难，偷偷下令，命令家家户户都把自己家门上的福字倒过来。

On New Year's Eve, the men sent by Emperor Zhu Yuan Zhang found that every family hung "Happiness"upside down, and could not find their target.

到了除夕晚上，朱元璋派出的人发现所有百姓家门上的福字都是倒着的，再也找不到说坏话的那户人家了。

中國民俗故事

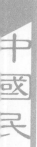

Emperor Zhu Yuan Zhang got the report, and shouted angrily, "The whole city was against me!"

朱元璋听了汇报，气急败坏地嚷道："哼！全城的人都在跟我作对！真是气死我了！"

Empress Ma advised him, " People who hang 'Happiness' upside down are looking forward to receiving great fortune and success in their life." She persuaded Zhu Yuan Zhang to listen to the people's opinion with an open mind.

马皇后急忙劝道:"皇上,老百姓把福字贴倒了,是希望福到,这是大吉大利呀。再说了,你也应该虚心接受别人的意见,这样才能当好皇帝。"

中國民俗故事

Emperor Zhu Yuan Zhang accepted Empress Ma's suggestions and ordered the people to hang "Happiness" upside down. And also, he became open to their suggestions and opinions.

朱元璋听了,觉得有道理,就下令以后所有的福字都倒着贴。他也开始接受别人的意见了。

From then on, all the people hang "Happiness" upside down during Chinese New Year. When others see it, they will say, "Happiness has arrived!"

从此，过年的时候大家都会在门上贴一个倒着的福字，别人看见了就会说："福到了，福到了！"

Walking on Stilts
踩 高 跷

In ancient China, people would gather in the city to celerbrate the Spring Festival. They would give performances to express their good wishes for the coming new year.

古时候，每逢春节，各地的人们都要聚在一起举办社火，热热闹闹地过大年。

But on one new year's eve, a greedy official took office in the city.

可是有一年春节，城里来了个贪官。

When the greedy official saw people preparing for the celebration, he began to think of ways he could profit from them, so he ordered his staff to put up a tollbridge at the city gate.

贪官看着忙碌的人群，于是打起了发财的主意。他命令衙役把城门的吊桥拉起来。

In the morning, performers of the country converged at the gate.

这天早晨，各村的社火队来到了城下。

The staff on the city wall shouted, "His Exellency has decreed that anyone who wants to cross the bridge must pay 50 grams of silver. Otherwise, no one may enter the city."

城墙上的衙役们对着社火队伍喊道："老爷有令，每人都得交一两过桥的银子，否则，不许进城！"

Having no other choice, people had to go home to pool money.

百姓们没办法，只得回家凑钱去了。

中國民俗故事

Everyone contributed as much money as they could and returned to the city gate. But the staff shouted, "His Exellency has decreed that anyone who wants to cross the bridge must pay 500 grams of silver at noon!"

大家东拼西凑，凑足了过桥费，又回到城下。不料，衙役们又喊道："老爷有令，中午过桥，每人得交十两银子。"

People didn't have so much money, they had to return home angrily.

百姓们哪有那么多钱，只好气愤地回家了。

The group leader was very worried. His son named Xiao Hu learnt of this, and decided to help his father.

社火队长回到家，愁眉不展。他的儿子小虎知道了这件事，决心帮父亲想办法。

"How to cross the deep moat?" Xiao Hu thought when he was looking at the long legs of a crane in the picture on the wall. Suddenly he got an idea.

"怎么才能跨过深深的护城河呢？"小虎一边看着自家墙上的仙鹤图，一边动脑筋。忽然，小虎盯上了仙鹤的长腿，立刻眼前一亮。

He ran into the yard, and made a pair of stilts with two long sticks. He tried, and they worked! So Xiao Hu told this method to his fellow villagers.

　　他赶忙跑到院子里，用两根结实、细长的木棍做成了一对高跷。试了试，果然管用。于是，小虎就把这个方法告诉了乡亲们。

The next day, people followed Xiao Hu's way and walked on stilts to cross the moat conveniently. The staff and the greedy official reached their wit's end.

第二天，百姓们都学着小虎的样子，踩着高跷来到了城下，毫不费力地跨过了护城河，进了城。衙役们和贪官见了，只能干瞪着眼，没有一点办法了。

From then on, the game of walking on stilts has been passed on and played even today.

从此以后，"踩高跷"就成为一种游戏流传了下来，一直到今天。

Door-God
门　神

In ancient times, there was an arched door formed by a huge peach tree in the Du Shuo Mountain in the East China Sea. A devil often came out through the door and went down to hurt people.

古时候，东海的度朔山上有棵巨大的桃树。有一个魔王时常从桃树弯成的拱门里溜出来祸害百姓。

The Jade Emperor learnt of this and ordered Generals Shen Tu and Yu Lei to guard the arched door and capture the devil.

玉皇大帝知道了，命令神荼和郁垒两个神将下凡，捉拿魔王。

Shen Tu and Yu Lei came to the Du Shuo Mountain, and waited for the devil nearby the arched door.

　　神荼、郁垒二神到了度朔山，守候在桃树拱门的旁边。

The devil walked out from the arched door as usual.

　　这天，魔王还像往常一样，大摇大摆地从拱门里溜出来。

Shen Tu and Yu Lei arrested the devil with magic, and sent him to the Jade Emperor. From then on, the devil couldn't hurt people again.

　　神荼、郁垒二神立刻施展魔法，把魔王捉住，交给了玉皇大帝，魔王再也不能祸害百姓了。

中國民俗故事

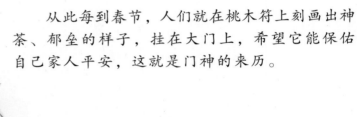

Since then, when Spring Festival comes, people draw the two generals Shen Tu and Yu Lei on peach wood and hang them on the doors to keep evils away. That is the origin of Door-God.

　　从此每到春节，人们就在桃木符上刻画出神荼、郁垒的样子，挂在大门上，希望它能保佑自己家人平安，这就是门神的来历。

Dragon Dance
耍龙灯

In the remote past, it rained heavily and relentlessly in one year, and many people were drowned.

古时候，有一年天降大雨，很多百姓都被洪水淹死了。

A kindhearted Dragon King was awoken by the people's cry.

好心的龙王被百姓们的哭喊声惊醒了。

Seeing the people in great distress, he decided to save them. So he flew to the heaven.

看到百姓们正遭受苦难，他决心拯救人们，于是腾云驾雾来到了天宫。

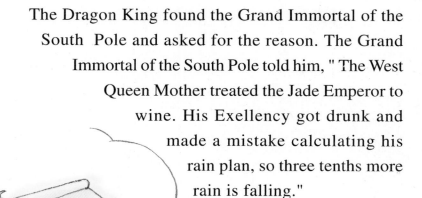

The Dragon King found the Grand Immortal of the South Pole and asked for the reason. The Grand Immortal of the South Pole told him, " The West Queen Mother treated the Jade Emperor to wine. His Exellency got drunk and made a mistake calculating his rain plan, so three tenths more rain is falling."

龙王找到南极仙翁，问及缘由。南极仙翁回答说："还不是玉皇大帝弄的？有一天，王母娘娘请他喝酒，他喝多了，写错了降雨簿，多写了三分降雨。"

中國民俗故事

The Dragon King learned the reason and slipped into the Jade Emperor's palace to correct the rain plan. After that, people's life got better.

龙王知道了原因，偷偷溜进王宫，改写了降雨簿，这下百姓们的日子就好过多了。

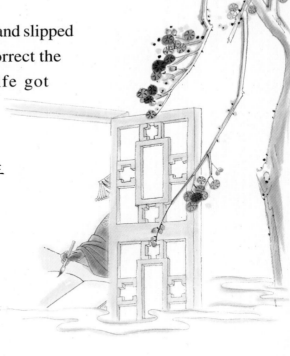

Unluckily, when the Jade Emperor realized the change, he was enraged and ordered sacred army to arrest the Dragon King.

不料，这件事不久就被玉皇大帝知道了，他非常恼火，立刻派天兵天将去捉拿龙王。

The sacred army found the Dragon King and the fight started. Even the Thunder God and the Lightning Goddess came to help the sacred army.

天兵天将找到龙王，施展法术，与龙王大战起来。一时间电闪雷鸣，雷公电母也来帮助天兵。

中國民俗故事

The Dragon King was no match for the attack. He transformed into a small bird and flew to the Jade Emperor's palace.

龙王抵挡不住，变成一只小鸟，飞进了天宫。

The small bird came to the Jade Emperor and claimed, "It was you who made the wrong rain plan, and people are gonna drown! Why are you trying to kill me?"

小鸟落到玉皇大帝面前，愤怒地质问："玉皇大帝，明明是你喝多了酒，写错了降雨簿，淹死了不少百姓。我帮你改正错误，你却来捉拿我？"

The Jade Emperor realized his fault and set the Dragon King free.

玉皇大帝听了，才知道是自己错了，于是释放了龙王。

Since then, people beat drums and gongs and do dragon dances on January 15 to commemorate the Dragon King.

后来，人们为了纪念龙王，每到正月十五，都会敲锣打鼓，耍起龙灯。

中國民俗故事

Writing Brush
毛　　笔

There was no pen or paper in ancient times, people just carved the words in bamboo and wood slips.

古时候最早是没有纸和笔的，人们在竹木简上刻字记事。

Meng Tian was a general of the State of Qin. One day, he won a victory, but there were no more bamboo slips to carve on. He would be killed if he didn't report it to the emperor in time.

蒙恬是战国时期秦国的大将。有一次，蒙恬打了个大胜仗，可是用来写奏章的竹简用光了，如果不及时给皇帝写奏章，是要被杀头的。

General Meng Tian was worried. He looked at the spear with a red tassel, and suddenly an idea came upon him.

蒙恬急得满头大汗，猛然间，他看见士兵手里的红缨枪，立刻有了个主意。

General Meng Tian tied a tassel on a stick, dipped it
in the ink and wrote his report on a piece of silk.
After writing, General Meng Tian did
not think the tassel worked well,
so he threw it into a lime pool.

蒙恬找来一缕红缨，将
它绑在一支小棍子上，蘸上
颜料，在绫子上写奏章。
写完后，蒙恬觉得红
缨太硬了，很不好用，便
将它扔进了石灰池。

Later, Emperor Shihuang ordered General
Meng Tian to build the Great Wall.

后来，秦始皇又命令蒙恬率领
十万民夫，修筑万里长城。

Expecting to complete the project earlier, General Meng Tian went to the construction site every day to hasten the workers.

蒙恬每天亲临现场指挥，只盼能早日修好长城。

Finally, the Great Wall was finished. But General Meng Tian met the trouble of writing report again.

终于有一天，长城修好了。可是，蒙恬又遇到了写奏章的麻烦。

General Meng Tian recalled the tassel, and scooped it from the lime pool. The tassel was softened by lime and was convenient to write with. So General Meng Tian named it "writing brush".

突然，他又想起了那缕红缨，于是赶忙把它从石灰池里捞起来。这时，红缨已经被石灰泡软了，写起字来非常方便。于是，蒙恬就给它命名为"笔"。

中國民俗故事

Later, General Meng Tian made many writing brushes with the hair from weasel tails, and people liked this kind of writing tool.

以后，蒙恬又用黄鼠狼尾巴上的狼毫制作了许多只笔，渐渐地，人们都喜欢上了这种书写工具。

After paper was invented in China, writing brushes began to have more uses. Later, many mills began to make writing brushes. General Meng Tian was greatly respected as the founder of writing brush.

等到人们发明纸后，毛笔的作用就更大了，而民间的制笔作坊就把蒙恬尊奉为毛笔的祖师爷。

Cai Sui
踩 岁

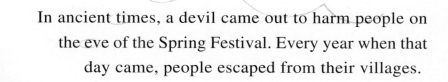

In ancient times, a devil came out to harm people on the eve of the Spring Festival. Every year when that day came, people escaped from their villages.

传说古时候有个妖怪，喜欢在大年三十的晚上出来祸害百姓。每到这天，人们就逃出村子躲灾。

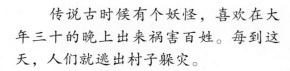

One year, when the Spring Festival was drawing near, a mother said to her son, "Son, the devil is coming. I am too old to run, you should run away yourself."

有一年，春节又快到了，母亲对儿子说："孩子，妖怪今晚就要来了，我老了，走不动了，你自己赶快逃命吧。"

"No, mum, I won't leave you behind."

"不！娘，你不走，我也不走。"儿子说。

中國民俗故事

"Mum, there is some sesame left, let's make some sesame cakes." The son found sesame stalks and beat them with a stick to get the seeds.

"娘，家里还有点芝麻，我给你做芝麻饼吃吧。"儿子说完，走出屋子，抱了一捆芝麻秸，用棍子噼噼啪啪地打了一些芝麻下来。

After eating, the son got a knife to abrade, and said, "Mum, I won't let the devil hurt you. If he comes, I will kill him!"

等母亲吃完了芝麻饼，儿子拿来了柴刀，一边磨刀一边对母亲说："娘，你放心，我不会让妖怪伤害你的，它要是来了，我就跟它拼了！"

At night, the devil came.

晚上，妖怪真的来了。

When the devil entered the yard, he stepped right onto the sesame stalks. Crack! Crack! The devil was scared of sound, and ran away.

　妖怪刚一踏进院子，就踩在了芝麻秸上，院子里立刻噼噼啪啪响个不停。妖怪是最怕声音的，听到这样的响声，吓得要死，赶紧逃跑了。

中國民俗故事

中國民俗故事

Since then, on every Spring Festival eve, children will put sesame stalks in the courtyard and step on them, Crack! Crack! This is "Cai Sui".

后来，每到春节，孩子们便会将芝麻秸铺在地上，踩出噼噼啪啪的响声，这就是"踩岁"。

God of Fortune
财 神 爷

In the Ming Dynasty, there was a treacherous court official named Yan Song. For his career, he presented his daughter to the emperor.

明朝时，有个大奸臣名叫严嵩，为了能够升官，主动把女儿献给了皇帝。

Because of the young maid, the emperor paid no attention to state affairs, drinking and partying every day, and let Yan Song decide everything.

有了美貌的妃子，皇帝从此不理朝政，每天只是陪她饮酒作乐，把一切政务都交给了严嵩。

With power in hand, Yan Song got very overbeared. All the civilian and military officers at court were resentful of him.

严嵩有了权力，便不把满朝的官员放在眼中，专横跋扈，欺压良善。对严嵩的所作所为，文武百官看在眼里，恨在心中。

At last, all the other civilian and military officers at court jointly required a punishment on Yan Song. Under the pressure, the emperor had to expel Yan Song from his office.

终于有一天，文武百官联名上书，在皇帝面前狠狠地告了严嵩一状。面对百官，皇帝也只能屈从，罢免了严嵩的官职，将他赶出了朝廷。

中國民俗故事

The emperor secretly gave Yan Song a gold bowl for begging.

不过，皇帝偷偷给了他一个用金子做的碗，让他讨饭用。

Having no other choice, Yan Song obeyed the order, and begged in the street.

没办法，严嵩只得领了圣命，拿着金碗沿街乞讨。

Yan Song begged in the street with his gold bowl. As he had done too many bad things, people who knew him didn't give him any food; those who didn't know him thought he was mad at the sight of the gold bowl in his hand.

　　严嵩来到大街上，拿着皇帝赐给他的金碗，向过路的行人乞讨。由于他过去做的坏事太多了，凡是认识他的人，都不会给他吃的；而那些不认识他的人，见他居然拿着金碗要饭，都以为他是个疯子。

中國民俗故事

Yan Song was starving after a whole day begging.

　　严嵩乞讨了一天，肚子饿得咕咕叫，却什么也没有要到。

Suddenly, a peddler was coming and shouting, "Beancurd for sale, beancurd for sale!"

　　忽然，大街上来了一个卖豆腐的小贩，边走边吆喝着："卖豆腐喽，卖豆腐喽，好吃的豆腐，快来买啊！"

Hearing this, Yan Song rushed over and said, "Please give me a piece of beancurd, I'm starving. I can trade this gold bowl with you."

　　饥肠辘辘的严嵩听见了叫卖声，赶忙跑上前去，说："求求你，请你给我一块豆腐吃吧，我都快饿死了。喏，我可以用这个金碗跟你换。"

中國民俗故事

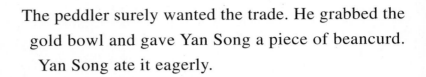

The peddler surely wanted the trade. He grabbed the gold bowl and gave Yan Song a piece of beancurd. Yan Song ate it eagerly.

小贩听了，当然愿意了。他接过金碗，递给严嵩一块豆腐。严嵩迫不及待地捧起豆腐，大口大口地吃起来。

But he swallowed so fast that he got choked and died. All the people were happy and said that the peddler did a good thing.

没想到，严嵩吃得太急了，豆腐卡住了他的喉咙，一下子噎死了。百姓们见了，高兴得不得了，都说小贩办了一件大好事。

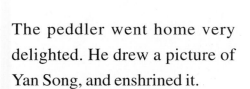

The peddler went home very delighted. He drew a picture of Yan Song, and enshrined it.

小贩高高兴兴地拿着金碗回到家，并且画了一张严嵩的画像，供奉了起来。

From then on, people followed him, enshrining Yan Song as the God of Fortune.

　　从此，百姓们也学着小贩的样子，开始把严嵩当作财神爷供奉起来了。

Land God
土 地 爷

It was said that immortal Han Xiang Zi was a nephew of Mr. Han. One day, Han Xiang Zi thought of his uncle, so he flew to Mr. Han's home.

传说，八仙之一的韩湘子是韩太公的侄子。这一天，韩湘子想起了叔叔，就下凡来到了韩太公的家中。

Grandpa Han was then in pursuit of perfection.

只见韩太公正坐在地上修炼，一付虔诚的样子。

Seeing his uncle so devoted, Han Xiang Zi decided to help him.

韩湘子见了，心想：叔叔可真是认真呀，看来他是真想成仙了。我来帮帮他吧。

Han Xiang Zi said to his uncle and aunt, "Dear uncle and aunt, I come to see you!"

韩湘子落下云头，走到叔叔、婶婶面前问候道："叔叔，婶婶，我来看你们来了。"

Grandpa Han held his hands and said, "Kid, help me! I want to be an immortal."

韩太公一见韩湘子，立刻拉住他的手说："孩子，是你呀！这回你可得帮我，我也想成仙！"

Han Xiang Zi smiled and said, "No problem, uncle, I will take you to the heaven if you are sincere enough."

韩湘子笑着说："没问题，叔叔，只要你心诚，我今天就带你去仙境。"

Grandpa Han interrupted Han Xiang Zi and said, "Wait! I have a payment of debt to demand! I can't go!"

韩太公突然打断韩湘子的话，说："慢着！我有一笔账还没要回来呢！怎么能走呢？"

Han Xiang Zi said, "Uncle, you have too many distracting thoughts, you can't become an immortal."So, he flew away.

韩湘子说："叔叔，你的杂念太多了，是成不了仙人的。"说完他驾起祥云，飞走了。

A couple years later, Han Xiang Zi came to see his uncle again.

几年后，韩湘子又来看望叔叔。

Seeing Han Xiang Zi, Grandpa Han said, "My nephew, I have eliminated all distracting thoughts. Bring me to the heaven."

见到韩湘子，韩太公急忙说："好侄子，我早已排除任何杂念，你快带我去仙境吧。"

Han Xiang Zi agreed to use magic.

韩湘子又答应了他。

"Wait! Wait!" said Grandpa Han," I almost forget that my son is going to take a test! I should go to say a few words to him. Otherwise, he will fail."

"慢着！慢着！"韩太公又喊道："我差点忘了。我儿子马上要去赶考了！我得去嘱咐嘱咐他。要不然，他准考不好！"

"Oh! uncle, how can you say you have eliminated all distracting thoughts! You should be in pursuit of perfection more! " Han Xiang Zi got angry and flew away.

"哎呀！叔叔，你的杂念还是太多，你还是再修练修炼吧！"韩湘子生气地看了看韩太公，驾起祥云，又飞走了。

Grandpa Han sighed and said, "Oh! It is so difficult to be an immortal!"

韩太公看着远去的韩湘子，叹了口气说："唉！成仙可真难啊！"

中國民俗故事

Several years later, Han Xiang Zi came again. Grandpa Han held his hand and said, "My nephew, I really have eliminated all distracting thoughts, so bring me to the heaven."

又过了好几年，韩湘子又来到了叔叔家。这一回，韩太公拉住他的手，信誓旦旦地说："好侄子，我现在真的把杂念去净了！不会再有什么杂念干扰我，你带我去仙境吧。"

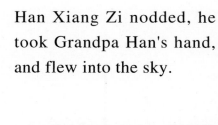

Han Xiang Zi nodded, he took Grandpa Han's hand, and flew into the sky.

　　韩湘子点点头，拉起韩太公的手，做起仙法，两人立刻升上了云端。

中國民俗故事

Grandpa Han was so glad to see the mountains and rivers beneath him, and thought, "It's so great! I will become an immortal! Oh, but how can I forget my wife!"

　　韩太公高兴坏了，低头看着地上的高山、河流，心想：太好了！我终于成仙了！从此以后，我就可以……糟糕！我怎么把老伴忘了！真该死！

"Stop! Stop! Han Xiang Zi, how about my wife?"

"停下！停下！韩湘子，我是成了仙，可我老伴怎么办呢？"韩太公嚷起来。

As soon as he thought of this, Grandpa Han fell down from the sky.

杂念一起，韩太公一下子就从云端掉了下来。

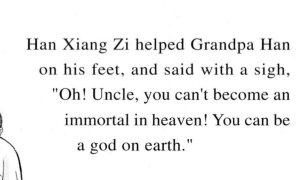

Han Xiang Zi helped Grandpa Han on his feet, and said with a sigh, "Oh! Uncle, you can't become an immortal in heaven! You can be a god on earth."

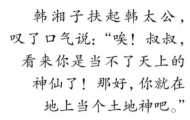

韩湘子扶起韩太公，叹了口气说："唉！叔叔，看来你是当不了天上的神仙了！那好，你就在地上当个土地神吧。"

So Grandpa Han became the Land God. Then he appointed his wife the Land Goddess.

于是，韩太公当了土地爷，他的老伴当上了土地奶奶。

图书在版编目 （CIP）数据

中国民俗故事（上）/赵杰改编；孙玉广等绘；郭冰珂译.
北京：海豚出版社，2005.10
ISBN 7-80138-539-X

I.中... II.①赵... ②孙... ③郭... III.图画故
事—中国—当代—英汉 IV. I287.8

中国版本图书馆 CIP 数据核字（2005）第 115086 号

中国民俗故事（上）

改编：赵　杰
绘画：孙玉广　张　明
翻译：郭冰珂
社址：北京百万庄大街 24 号　　　　　邮编：100037
印刷：北京雷杰印刷有限公司
开本：16 开（787 毫米×1092 毫米）
文种：英汉　印张：4
版次：2005 年 10 月第 1 版　2006 年 12 月第 3 次印刷
标准书号：ISBN 7-80138-539-X
定价：20.00 元